Clan MacScotch and the Angel's Share

Alison Mary Fitt & Keith Robson

First published in Great Britain 2011

Design - Melvin Creative
Printing - Printer Trento, Italy

Published by
GW Publishing
PO Box 6091
Thatcham
Berks
RG19 8XZ.

Tel + 44 (0)1635 268080
www.gwpublishing.com

ISBN 978-0-9561211-7-2

Clan MacScotch and the Angel's Share

Dedicated to whisky craftsmen throughout Scotland

Main Characters

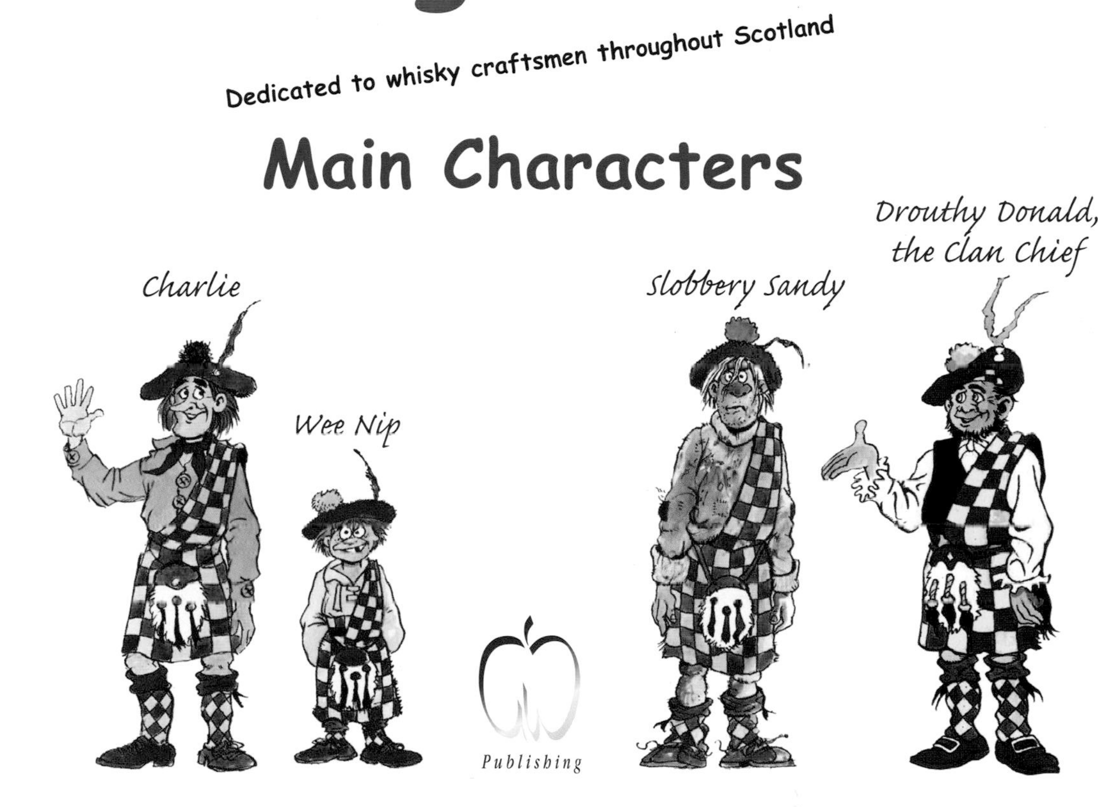

For centuries, crofters across the length and breadth of Scotland put their excess barley to good use by making what they called "uisge beatha"; a warming drink that helped keep the cold nights at bay.

Enterprising Clan MacScotch made their whisky in a cave on the shores of Loch Dram. They came up with the idea of storing their precious drink in barrels, and began to notice a big improvement in the taste.

Eventually, after much creeping about, the Chief, Drouthy Donald, had good news for his clansmen.

But making whisky secretly and not paying tax on it to the greedy government wasn't exactly a doddle, and there were always challenges. Rainwater would sometimes leak through a crack in the cave roof, and dribble onto their precious store of peat.

With the peat being so damp, the fire's no' lighting. But we need a guid hot fire tae heat the stills. Give it a blaw, Charlie...

These fire-lichters should help, Chief.

With much huffing and puffing they would get the fire going, but the damp peat made it very smoky. More worryingly, the smoke bellowed out of the cave and could be seen for miles around.

Their main concern was that the local excise man would see the smoke and come to investigate. Whenever word came that he was approaching, frantic activity would ensue, as rocks were heaved into place to conceal the cave mouth.

Hurry, lads - old Snoopy's on his way

Pile them up abody. It's a richt slog having tae dae this. But we canna let him find oot what we've been up tae.

Usually, when the taxman showed up, Clan MacScotch would stand around, looking as if butter wouldn't melt in their mouths. Owing to their cunning at arranging the rocks, there was no cave or tell-tale wisp of smoke to be seen.

On one occasion, however, when he had been passing through, some drops of a strong-smelling liquid were noticed on the ground. The taxman, who had a nose like a bloodhound, bent to sniff it.
"It's whisky alright," he declared. "Where has it come from?"

"We haven't a clue, Mr Snoop. It's not oors! Please say ye believe us," begged the worried clansmen. However, much to their relief, the source of the spillage was soon traced.

Now at last, there was some serious celebrating to do. First, however, the Chief had an errand to run.

"I'm off to Oban to buy a silver quaich," he announced." We shall fill it with the very first drops from the barrel, and drink a toast to our own glorious MacScotch this very evening. I won't be long, lads."

The clansmen told him to take his time.

The thirsty clansmen had another reason for urging Drouthy Donald not to hurry back. It gave them ample time to sneak some whisky while he was away. As the Chief rode off, they hot-footed it to the cave, desperate for a first swallow of the braw liquid.

But it looked like they would have to wait a bit longer. For, try as they might, they couldn't remove the bung from the barrel. Even Charlie, who had the longest finger nails, couldn't prise it out.

MAC SCOTCH

It's nae use, lads. It winna budge.

All that lovely whisky in there, and we canna get it oot.

It's enough tae make ye greet!

A corkscrew, they reckoned, would definitely do the job. But the only person who owned one was Drouthy Donald. So the ever resourceful Charlie went to ask the Chief's wife, Thirsty Kirsty, if he could borrow it. "I need it to ready some new casks," he fibbed. But Kirsty couldn't find the corkscrew anywhere.
Sorry, Charlie. It's no' in oor cutlery drawer, where it should be. That man o' mine never puts onything back in its richt place. I've scoured the rest o' the hoose for it tae.
Dinna worry, Kirsty. Thanks for looking onyway.
He's no' having ony luck, Sandy!

With no corkscrew to be had, the thirsty clansmen gave the barrel a canny wee pry with a screwdriver, hoping that would slacken the bung.
Cross yir fingers that it works, abody.
This isna the richt tool, but maybe it will dae the job, lads.
MAC SCOTCH
I'm crossing ma een, as well as ma fingers.

But annoyingly, the bung remained firmly in place. Growing more desperate by the minute, the clansmen tied one end of a long piece of string to the bung, and the other end to a rock. Then they rolled the barrel forward, hoping that this would yank the bung out.
This should do the trick.
Dae ye hear aw that braw whisky sloshing aboot?
I'm dyin' fur a swally..
Me tae. My tongue's hingin' oot.
That barrel must be full o' fish for us tae eat, Salty!
Dinna be sae gullible. When did that lot ever feed us?

Unfortunately for them, the string snapped, and the barrel hurtled off down a brae, causing havoc as it went. With the clansmen chasing after it, it rollicked onwards, flegging the wits out of some hens and almost running over poor Dewar, the clan cat.

Its trail of destruction continued, with the clansmen, who weren't the fittest of blokes, puffing and panting after it in vain. The barrel seemed to have taken on a life of its own. It sent a dustbin flying, then demolished a line of washing strung out on the shore.

Finally, with a muckle great splash, the barrel went skelping into Loch Dram.

"We'll hae tae paddle in after it," gasped Charlie. "Boots off, lads!"

But the panic-stricken clansmen were in such a state, it took them forever to undo their bootlaces.

However, as a brisk sea breeze was blowing the barrel further out, retrieving it by boat was soon the only option.

The clansmen rowed frantically - only too aware of the trouble they would be in if they lost the Chief's precious whisky for ever.

After a mammoth rowing session, they finally caught up with the seaweed-covered cask. But when Muckle Malty, the heftiest clansman, leaned over to grab it, his end of the boat tipped down alarmingly and...

... as anticipated, they all landed in the freezing loch.

Some of the clansmen, who couldn't swim a stroke - but now wished that they had bothered to learn - thrashed around in the water, convinced that their number was up.

However, Charlie knew how to spur them on.
"What are ye thinking aboot?" he asked them. "Ye canna droon withoot a taste of oor braw MacScotch whisky, now can ye?"

It was the encouragement they needed, and, keeping their eyes firmly fixed on the barrel as Charlie instructed, the floundering clansmen eventually made it to the shore.

Safely back on dry land, the clansmen were hugely relieved that the barrel of whisky had been rescued. Soaked and shivering, they were more in need of some of its contents than ever.

Once they had scraped the seaweed off the barrel, they had another go at removing the bung. But it seemed more jammed than ever.
What's it stuck wi'-cement? Sorry tae disappoint ye, lads. But at least we've got the barrel back.
Aye, but the whisky's INside, and we're OOTside. What guid is that?
We'll never get w-warmed up at this rate.
MAC SCOTCH

Exhausted and fed-up the clansmen collapsed on any seat they could find. But as Wee Nip was about to plonk himself down onto a sack of barley, he gave an excited yelp. There, in front of his eyes, was the missing corkscrew!
Look what I found, lads! I nearly sat on it!
It's the cork-screw! Yipee! The chief must have left it there to open the bung with tonight.
Good on ye, Wee Nip. That's the best find since Columbus discovered America!
MAC SCOTCH

In no time at all, the jubilant clansmen had removed the bung and were lined up with their mugs to sample the whisky. They sniffed the air and pondered: Floral? Honeyed? Smoky? Peaty? The smell made them even more desperate for a drink of it.
That's mair than a nip.
A wee nip for wee Nip! I canna wait!
Nae shoving. This isna the winter sales. Ye'll aw get a dram.
CB

Their ordeal in the loch forgotten, they were soon knocking back the rich, golden liquid with relish.
MacScotch on the rocks- nothing like it!
I belong tae Glasgow .. tra-la..
Oh flooer o Scotland... traa-lee..
It disna half warm ye up!
Here's tae the water o life!
It's braw stuff alricht. Let's hae a wee re-fill.
CB
MAC SCOTCH

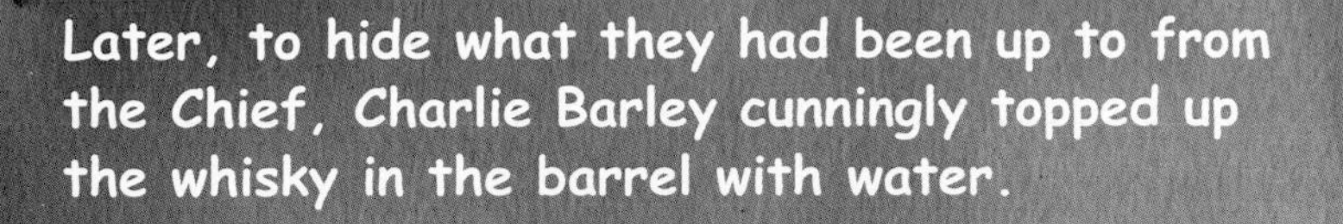

Later, to hide what they had been up to from the Chief, Charlie Barley cunningly topped up the whisky in the barrel with water.

To be on the safe side, in another crafty move, the clansmen had haggis and chips, with lashings of vinegar, for their tea. The last thing they wanted was Drouthy Donald smelling whisky on their breath.

When Drouthy Donald returned, the clansmen made a great show of admiring the quaich, and told him how much they were looking forward to sampling the whisky.

But when the Chief tapped the barrel to get their attention and to make a speech, he was puzzled.

"I expected the level to be down a wee bit, but not as much as this," he muttered. "How can this be?"

Charlie and the clansmen knew. They had drunk more whisky than they realised, and hadn't put enough water back in.

Not surprisingly, the Chief was suspicious.
"Have you lot been at it behind my back?" he demanded.
"Oh no, Chief," they protested. "We wouldna do a sneaky thing like that!"

To prove their innocence, they invited him to smell their breath.

"Hmmmm! You all reek of vinegar," grunted Drouthy Donald. "Are you sure you didn't smother your chips in it to disguise the smell of whisky?"

"Certainly not," Charlie told him. "How can you think such a thing? We aye droon oor chips in vinegar because it gives them mair flavour."
The Chief still wasn't convinced they were telling the truth, so quick- thinking Charlie told him they had seen an angel at the whisky!
"You've heard o' the angel's share, Chief?"

Much to their relief, it seemed as if the chief had swallowed Charlie's yarn. Smiling affably, Drouthy Donald invited his clansmen to join him in toasting their own wonderful uisge beatha. As they gathered round with raised mugs, they could hardly keep their faces straight.

Afterwards, they couldn't stop sniggering and Charlie was the hero of the hour. It seemed as if his inventive skills had got them off the hook.
But the Chief had his own thoughts on the matter.
What a bunch of chancers they are. Do they thinkI was born yesterday?
Ye're a genious, Charlie. An angel? How did ye come up with that porkie?
Oh, it wis jist aff the tap o' ma heid. My teacher aye said I had a guid imagination...
It was a real cracker...
MAC SCOTCH

That evening, as the whisky flowed and Clan MacScotch partied beside Loch Dram, singing the old songs of Scotland and growing merrier by the minute, an unexpected visitor dropped in on their celebrations.

The clansmen weren't at all happy to see her … especially when she told the Chief it was them who had been at the barrel!

Next morning, the clansmen had hangovers as big as Ben Nevis. As if that didn't make them miserable enough, they discovered that the Chief had clapped a padlock and chains on the whisky barrel.

"I'm glad our heavenly friend blew the whistle on you," he told them sternly. "Ye'll no' be thieving any more whisky when my back's turned."

"But we didna," they protested. "Come on, Chief! Ye surely dinna believe yon angel was real? Ye can see gey queer things when ye've dooned a few drams!"

But Drouthy Donald decided it was payback time for all the claptrap his clansmen — Charlie Barley in particular — had been giving him.

So that angel wisna real, eh? Weel, how do we account for this tartan sash which was left on the ground after she disappeared? It's awfie like the one she was wearing...

Think o' an explanation quick, Charlie.

I canna, lads- no' this time. Ma heid's ower sair wi' aw that whisky

He's jist windin them up. That sash belonged tae ma granny who was a member o' anither clan. It resembles the angel's one richt enough....

MAC SCOTCH

For once, Charlie was stuck for words!

Some words you might need to know...

The Angels Share - As the spirit matures in oak casks, a small percentage seeps through the pour wood and evaporates into the atmosphere.
This "missing" liquid is affectionately referred to as the Angels Share!

abody	everyone
aboot	about
ain	own
awfie	awfully
aye	yes
aye	always
backie	transportation on back
bilin mad	very angry
blaw	blow
bocht	bought
braw	great
canna	can not
cannie	careful
cauld	cold
cowpin	overbalancing
crabbit	bad-tempered
dae	do
didna	did not
disna	does not
doon	down
dooned	downed
drappie	drop
drookit	drenched
droon	drown
een	eyes
flooer	flower
fur	for
gey queer	very odd
guid	good
hae	have
heid	head
hingin	hanging
isna	is not
jiggin	dancing
jist	just
lichter	lighter
ma	my
mak	make
mair	more
mooth	mouth
nae	no
noo	now
o'	of
oot	out
onyway	anyway
ower sair	too sore
pauchled	pinched
richt	right
sicht	sight
sup	drink
swally	swallow
tae	too
tap	top
thocht	thought
thrapple	throat
weel	well
wee	small
whack it	beat it
wha's	who is
whaur	where
wi'	with
wifie	woman
winna	will not
wull	will
ye	you
ye'll	you will
yon	that